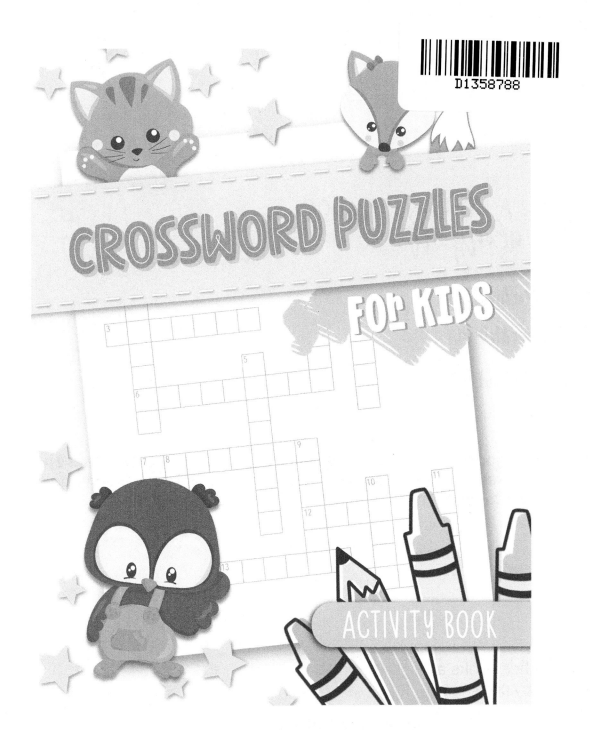

CROSSWORD PUZZLES

For KIDS

ACTIVITY BOOK

This Book Belongs to:

FOR A LITTLE INSPIRATION
follow along at:

◉ @JUNEANDLUCY

𝙛 @JUNEANDLUCY

WWW. JUNELUCY.COM

✉ **Love free goodies?** Join our newsletter by emailing us at **freebies@junelucy.com** to receive freebies, discounts and sales info. Let us know which book you bought by putting the book title in the subject line of your email.

Shop our other books at
www.junelucy.com

For questions and customer service, email us at
support@junelucy.com

ZOO ANIMALS

ACROSS
3. This bird waddles in the cold.
4. Has wings and a beak.
6. Large reptile with sharp teeth and long tail.
7. Has a trunk and tusks.
12. Large, striped cat in Asia.
13. Animal that eats bananas.
14. Black and white bear.

DOWN
1. Large, very fast cat.
2. Has a long neck to eat leaves.
4. Type of this animal includes panda and grizzly.
5. This animal has a pouch for its joey.
8. King of the jungle.
9. Reptile that moves slowly.
10. Animal with black and white stripes.
11. A marsupial that eats eucalyptus.

ZOO ANIMALS

1 (down) CHEETAH

2 (down) GIRAFFE

3 (across) PENGUIN

4 (across) BIRD — **4 (down)** BEAR

5 (down) KANGAROO

6 (across) ALLIGATOR

7 (across) ELEPHANT — **8 (down)** LION

9 (down) TURTLE

10 (down) ZEBRA

11 (down) KOALA

12 (across) TIGER

13 (across) MONKEY

14 (across) PANDA

FRUIT

ACROSS
1. Jam is often made from this red fruit.
5. This sour fruit is similar to an orange.
8. This summer fruit has black seeds.
9. This tart fruit is yellow.
10. Make a cobbler with this stone fruit.
11. A small, fuzzy fruit.
13. This fruit is also a color.
14. You give this fruit to a teacher.

DOWN
2. Veruca Salt turned into this.
3. This red fruit has a hard pit.
4. This red fruit has up to 200 tiny seeds.
6. This spiky fruit wears a green crown.
7. Monkeys love this fruit.
9. Use this green fruit to make a tart pie.
12. These fruits come in a bunch.

FRUIT

DAY AT THE BEACH

ACROSS
4. This sweet fruit comes from a palm tree.
5. You collect these on the beach.
7. A frozen treat on a stick.
9. Don't get pinched by this crustacean.
10. These shield your eyes from the sun.
12. Tall object that shields you from the sun.
13. A person who keeps swimmers safe.
14. Use this to dry off.
15. Try to spot the fin of this aquatic mammal.

DOWN
1. Catch these while surfing.
2. Construct this building in the sand.
3. This liquid protects your skin from UV rays.
6. Grainy material that you dig in.
8. Set up a net and play this beach sport.
11. Beach bird.

DAY AT THE BEACH

Across / Down crossword puzzle:

- 1. W A V E S (down)
- 2. C A S T L E (down)
- 3. S U N S C R E E N (down)
- 4. C O C O N U T (across)
- 5. S H E L L S (across)
- 6. S A N D (down)
- 7. P O P S I C L E (across)
- 8. V O L L E Y B A L L (down)
- 9. C R A B (across)
- 10. S U N G L A S S E S (across)
- 11. S E A G U L L (down)
- 12. U M B R E L L A (across)
- 13. L I F E G U A R D (across)
- 14. T O W E L (across)
- 15. D O L P H I N (across)

SPORTS

ACROSS
2. Doing the backstroke or butterfly.
5. Score a touchdown to win this game.
7. Use a racket to play this singles or doubles game.
8. When the marching band performs.
9. The leader of a sports team.
12. Sport with an orange ball and two nets.
13. The ref blows this to make a call.
15. A winning team may be awarded this.

DOWN
1. Where you might play soccer or baseball.
3. Bump, set, and spike in this sport.
4. What a player wears.
6. Run laps around this.
10. Person who officiates a game.
11. Throw this object through a hoop for two points.
14. Sport of the World Cup.

SPORTS

Across:
- 2. SWIMMING
- 7. TENNIS
- 8. HALFTIME
- 9. COACH
- 12. BASKETBALL
- 13. WHISTLE
- 15. TROPHY
- 5. FOOTBALL

Down:
- 1. FIELD
- 3. VOLLEYBALL
- 4. UNIFORM
- 6. TRACK
- 10. REFEREE
- 11. BALL
- 14. SOCCER

TRANSPORTATION

ACROSS

1. A vehicle that transports large groups of people on the road.
3. Drive this 4-wheeled vehicle on the road.
6. This carries people on objects by sea.
9. A big, public road.
10. Two-wheeled motorized vehicle.
12. Pedestrians walk on this next to the road.
14. This transportation has many cars, including a caboose.

DOWN

2. This transportation system goes underground.
4. Train tracks make up this system.
5. Big machine driven on a farm.
7. Kids love to ride these objects with two wheels.
8. Travel in the sky in this.
11. Pioneers travelled in these.
13. Paddle in this small boat.

TRANSPORTATION

LUNCHTIME

ACROSS

3. You wipe your mouth with it.
4. Spread this on a sandwich with peanut butter.
8. Main course made with two slices of bread.
9. This cup often comes with your lunchbox.
11. Types of this dessert include chocolate chip and oatmeal.
13. Meal made of lettuce and chopped veggies.
14. Drink with lots of calcium.
15. Sweet fruits that come in a bunch.

DOWN

1. Typical lunch hour.
2. Sip this drink made from fruit.
5. Where you store your mid-day meal.
6. Crunchy veggies cut into sticks.
7. Pull your chair up to this to eat.
10. Dunk your carrots or pita in this chickpea dip.
12. A crunchy, salty snack sometimes made with potatoes.

LUNCHTIME

WEATHER

ACROSS
4. Season known for snow.
6. Pellets of frozen rain that can be as big as a baseball.
9. Device that measures temperature.
11. Twirling column of air caused by a storm.
12. Movement of air, like a breeze or a gust.
13. The amount of water vapor in the air.
14. Formation with types including cumulus and cirrus.

DOWN
1. Flurries of ice crystals that fall when it's cold.
2. Water droplets that fall from the sky.
3. Profession that involves predicting weather.
5. The sound caused by lightning.
7. Electrostatic bolt that occurs during a storm.
8. A meteorologist's prediction.
10. Spot this colorful arc after it rains.

WEATHER

THE COLOR BLUE

ACROSS
2. Bright bird that sometimes talks.
5. Small, round fruit often found in muffins.
7. This swimming animal is the largest known mammal.
9. Types of this include rose and daisy.
11. The organs that help us see .
13. Large bird with bright feathers.
14. These blue pants have been around since the 1800s.

DOWN
1. Blue gemstone.
3. Insect with colorful wings.
4. The atmosphere above the earth containing clouds.
5. Fill this with helium and watch it float.
6. Particle of water that falls from the sky.
8. Color a picture with this waxy object.
10. Large body of saltwater.
12. Take a dive or swim some laps in one of these.

THE COLOR BLUE

OCEAN ANIMALS

ACROSS

3. This animal is the largest on Earth.
4. Don't get pinched by this grumpy crustacean.
6. With a long, barbed tail, this animal swims close to the ocean floor.
7. This long fish could be electric!
8. Named after a pony, males of this species carry the babies.
9. Watch out for the long, stinging tentacles of this animal.
11. Types of this animal are great white and tiger.
12. This sea reptile has a shell for protection.
13. This small crustacean is food for a lot of sea animals.

DOWN

1. This playful mammal lives in a pod.
2. This eight-legged octopod is thought to have a high IQ.
4. This colorful object makes up a reef.
5. Types of this animal include flounder and trout.
6. With five legs, this animal is shaped like an object in the sky.
10. This clawed animal may be served in a fancy restaurant.

OCEAN ANIMALS

SNACKS

ACROSS

1. Types of these snacks include tortilla and potato.
3. These fruits come in a bunch.
4. These salty snacks are known for their twisted shape.
5. Take this snack of nuts, raisins, and chocolate on a hike. (two words)
7. Add peanut butter and raisins to this veggie to make "ants on a log."
9. Slice up this fruit for a crunchy snack.
10. A slice of cheese on these makes a great snack.
11. These oval nuts are packed with protein.
12. Dunk your pita bread or carrots in this chickpea dip.

DOWN

1. Dairy snack made of cow milk, sheep milk, or goat milk.
2. This microwaved snack is great during a movie.
4. This snack comes creamy or crunchy. (two words)
6. Pair this crunchy snack with yogurt or eat it as a bar.
7. Types of these snacks include chocolate chip and sugar.
8. Rabbits love to snack on these crunchy veggies.

SNACKS

A crossword puzzle with the following filled-in answers:

1. CHIPS (across)
2. POPCORN (down)
3. GRAPES (across)
4. PRETZELS (across)
5. TRAILMIX (across)
6. GRANOLA (down)
7. CELERY (across)
8. CARROTS (down)
9. APPLE (across)
10. CRACKERS (across)
11. ALMONDS (across)
12. HUMMUS (across)

Additional down words: CHEESE, PEANUTBUTTER, COOKIES

THE SOLAR SYSTEM

ACROSS

2. The center of our solar system.
4. This planet is known for its rings.
6. The planet where humans live.
7. The event when the Moon's shadow crosses the Earth's surface.
9. Minor planets orbit in this 'belt'.
10. Instrument used to see things far away in space.
12. There are eight of these in our solar system, including Mars and Venus.
13. Neil Armstrong is the first person to walk on this.

DOWN

1. Also known as the 'Red Planet'.
2. These balls of gas twinkle in the night sky.
3. The closest planet to the Sun.
5. A person trained to go into space.
8. A manmade object placed into orbit for research, such as Sputnik.
11. This used to be the smallest planet but it was reclassified as a dwarf planet.

THE SOLAR SYSTEM

WINTER WORDS

ACROSS

2. Frozen ice crystals that fall from the sky.
4. Fun activity where you ride an object down a hill.
7. Build this with snow and don't forget the carrot nose.
8. This sweet cocoa drink will keep you warm. (Two words)
10. Where you might toast a marshmallow.
11. Wear these on your feet to glide on a frozen pond. (Two words)
14. Some people chop down their own during the holidays.

DOWN

1. Santa's helpers.
3. A decorative object you place on a Christmas tree.
4. Throw these cold objects during a playful outdoor fight.
5. Make a tasty house out of this spiced cookie.
6. A house made out of snow.
9. Spikes of ice that form when dripping water freezes.
12. This jolly old man delivers presents.
13. Wrap this around your neck to stay warm.

WINTER WORDS

1 ELVES
2 SNOW
3 ORNAMENT
4 SLEDDING
4 SNOWBALLS
5 GINGERBREAD
6 IGLOO
7 SNOWMAN
8 HOTCHOCOLATE
9 ICICLES
10 FIREPLACE
11 ICESKATES
12 SANTA
13 SCARF
14 TREE

LET'S GO ON A PICNIC

ACROSS

2. Hopefully these insects don't show up to your picnic.
6. A beef patty on a bun.
8. Lay down a red and white checkered one for your picnic.
9. You sit on this at a picnic table.
10. Eat under one of these for some shade.
11. Finish your meal with a slice of this apple dessert.
12. Where you keep your cold foods.
13. Put this in your drink to keep it cool.

DOWN

1. A public area where you might have a picnic.
3. The ideal season for a picnic.
4. These bright lights might explode in the sky at night.
5. Two pieces of bread with meat and cheese.
7. Condiment for a hot dog.
8. What you might carry your picnic lunch in.
9. A sandy picnic might take place here.

LET'S GO ON A PICNIC

PLANTS AND FLOWERS

ACROSS

2. What you plant in the ground to make plants and flowers.
6. The colorful parts of the top of a flower.
7. The sun provides this to help plants grow.
8. The system that helps water a lawn.
9. Liquid required for photosynthesis.
11. Bees get this from plants.
12. Parts of the plants that absorb water and minerals for the stem.
13. Types of this plant include oak, elm, and palm.

DOWN

1. These grow from a plant's stem and help with photosynthesis.
3. Part of the plant that supports the leaves, flowers, and fruit.
4. Plant your flower in this to provide it nutrients.
5. Adding this to soil helps your plants grow.
8. This plant can be found in the ocean.
10. These flowers are often given on Valentine's Day.

PLANTS AND FLOWERS

PETS

ACROSS

3. Take your dog on a daily one of these for exercise.
4. Make sure this orange, swimming pet has a big tank.
7. Pet that says, "Meow!".
9. This bird can learn up to 1,000 words.
10. This furry pet likes to sniff and hop.
13. A small, colorful member of the parrot family.
15. A young cat.

DOWN

1. A small reptile with a long tail that eats bugs.
2. Pet that says, 'Woof!' and loves bones.
5. This small crustacean carries its home on its back. (Two words)
6. What you call a baby dog.
8. This reptile pet walks very slowly.
11. When your pet is dirty, you give them one of these.
12. Put a wheel and water bottle in this rodent's cage.
14. Take your sick pet to this place.

PETS

HALLOWEEN

ACROSS
1. Dress up as this by wearing a big, white sheet.
3. Carve this to make a Jack-o'-lantern.
5. What a spider spins.
6. What kids get when trick-or-treating.
7. A famous vampire.
10. The undead.
12. This animal says, 'Hoo! Hoo!'.
14. Frightening.

DOWN
2. Kids yell this when someone answers the door. (3 words)
4. All wrapped up and found in Egypt.
5. She might cast a spell with her cauldron.
8. Bob for these in a fall game.
9. Where a vampire sleeps.
11. What a witch rides.
13. This animal flies at night looking for mosquitos.

HALLOWEEN

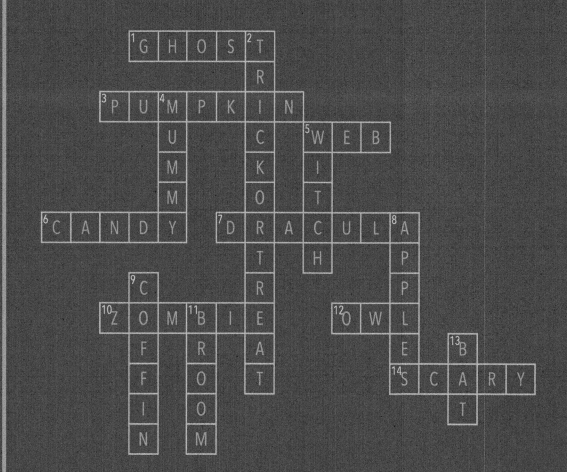

Across and down crossword solution:

- 1 GHOST
- 2 TRICKORTREAT
- 3 PUMPKIN
- 4 MUMMY
- 5 WEB / WITCH
- 6 CANDY
- 7 DRACULA
- 8 APPLE
- 9 COFFIN
- 10 ZOMBIE
- 11 BROOM
- 12 OWL
- 13 BAT
- 14 SCARY

AT THE FARM

ACROSS
3. Where the chickens might live.
5. A baby pig.
7. What horses eat.
9. What a pig says.
10. Lays eggs.
12. Where all the pigs are.
13. Person who tends to the animals and fields.
15. Provides milk on a dairy farm.

DOWN
1. This animal says, 'Neigh!'.
2. What pigs may eat.
4. Where the animals are kept on a farm.
6. Farmer rides this to tend to the field.
8. Says, 'Hee-haw!'.
11. This bearded animal says, 'Baa!'.
14. What a cow says.

AT THE FARM

```
                              1
                              H
   2              3
   S              C  O  O  P
   L              O
   O              R              4
  5               S           7  B
   P  I  G  L  E  T        H  A  Y
                  R        D     R
                  A     9  O  I  N  K
          10      C  H  I  C  K  E  N
          11                      N
           G                      K
           O                   12
                               P  E  N
  13                14            Y
   F  A  R  M  E  R
           T        O
          15        C  O  W
```

AUTUMN WORDS

ACROSS
  3. Wear a wool one to keep warm.
  4. Carve this orange gourd.
  5. Another word for autumn.
  7. Holiday in November with lots of food.
  9. How the air feels in autumn.
  12. Wear this around your neck in cold weather.
  13. The month after Thanksgiving.
  14. Pick this red fruit from a tree in fall.

DOWN
  1. The nut from an oak tree.
  2. Popular fall dessert, served in slices.
  3. Eat this with your turkey.
  6. This spice is used in fall desserts or tea.
  8. Holiday where kids dress up in costume.
  10. A tour given with a tractor on a farm or pumpkin patch.
  11. The main course on Thanksgiving.

AUTUMN WORDS

COLORS

ACROSS
2. Color of the gemstone sapphire.
3. This shade of bright green is also a fruit.
5. Color of grass.
9. This color is also the name of a fruit.
12. The darkest color.
13. Colorful spectrum of light in the sky after it rains.
14. The color of the sky on a gloomy day.

DOWN
1. Color of an apple.
2. The color of dirt.
4. A deep shade of red.
6. Shade of bright blue that is used in jewelry.
7. The color of a ripe banana.
8. Bubble gum is often this color.
10. Grapes often come in this color.
11. A shiny precious metal, along with gold.

COLORS

BABY ANIMALS

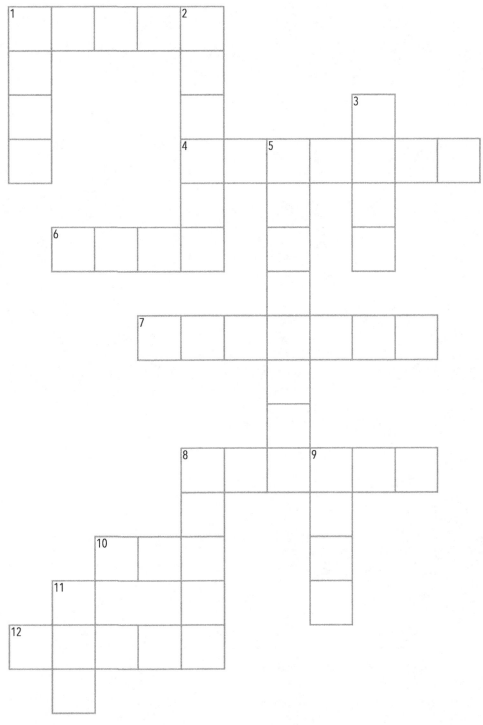

ACROSS
1. A baby chicken.
4. A baby frog.
6. A baby deer.
7. A baby goose.
8. A baby pig.
10. A baby seal.
12. A baby rabbit.

DOWN
1. A baby cow.
2. A baby cat.
3. A baby kangaroo.
5. A baby duck.
8. A baby dog.
9. A baby sheep.
11. A baby bear.

BABY ANIMALS

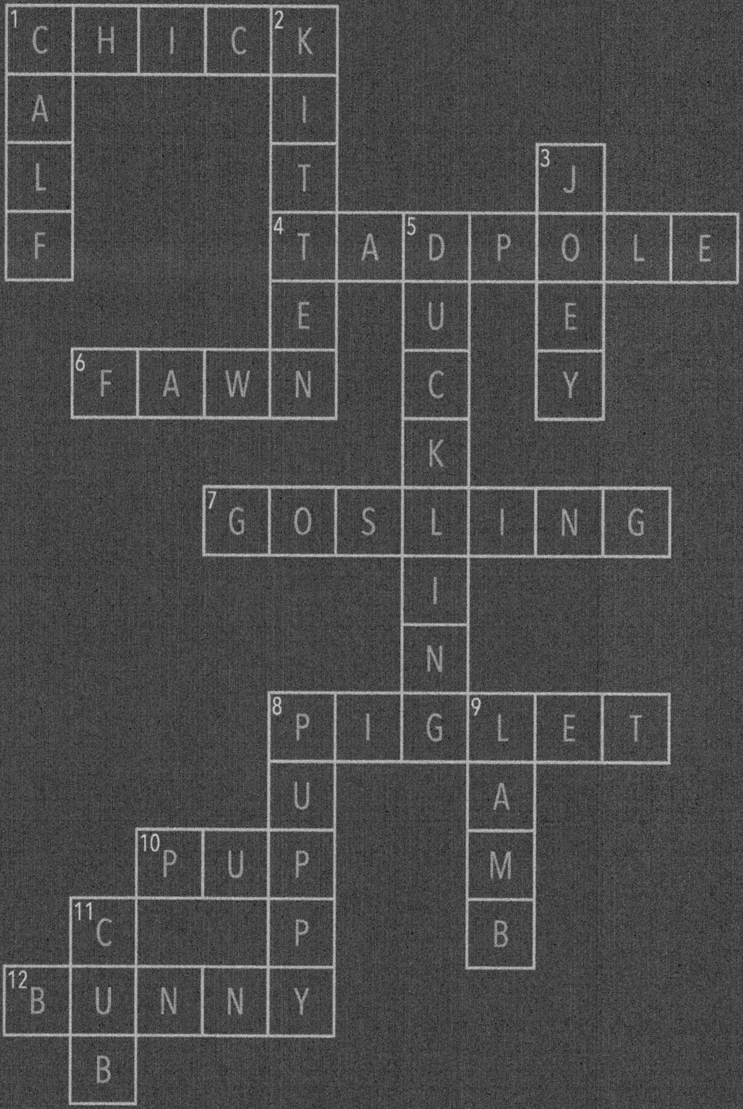

1 CHICK
1 CALF
2 KITTEN
3 JOEY
4 TADPOLE
5 DUCKLING
6 FAWN
7 GOSLING
8 PIGLET
8 PUPPY
9 LAMB
10 PUP
11 CUB
12 BUNNY

PARTS OF THE BODY

ACROSS
1. Connects the head to the body.
4. Use this to breathe and smell.
6. Grows out of your head.
7. Use these to grab and touch things.
12. Use them to hear sounds.
13. Has an iris and a retina.
14. Joint connecting the hand to the forearm.

DOWN
2. Joint in the middle of the leg.
3. Use this to speak.
4. Hard covering that protects fingers and toes.
5. The fingers are connected to these.
8. Joint in the middle of the arm.
9. These help walk.
10. Ten of these extend from the feet.
11. Made of the femur, fibula, tibia, and patella.

PARTS OF THE BODY

									¹N	E	C	K	²K
						³M							N
						O							E
						U			⁴N	O	S	E	E
						T			A				
				⁵H		⁶H	A	I	R				
				A					L				
			⁷F	I	N	G	E	R	S				
		⁹F		D		⁸E					¹⁰T		
¹¹L		¹²E	A	R	S	L					O		
¹³E	Y	E				B					E		
G		T				O							
S						¹⁴W	R	I	S	T			

SUMMER FUN

ACROSS
  2. Protects your skin from UV rays.
  6. Dry off with this.
  7. Pack up the car and go on this vacation.
     (2 words)
  8. Summer sandals. (2 words)
  11. Summer fruit with red flesh and black seeds.
  12. A packed lunch eaten in the park.
  14. Tart summer drink.

DOWN
  1. A holiday trip to a special destination.
  2. These protect the eyes from sunshine.
  3. Kids ride this object with two wheels.
  4. Summer activity in the water.
  5. Where a lifeguard works.
  9. Frozen dessert on a stick.
  10. Frozen dairy treat. (2 words)
  13. Location with ocean and sand.

SUMMER FUN

HOLIDAYS

ACROSS
  2. Jewish celebration lasting 8 days and nights.
  6. Celebrated the day you were born.
  9. Blow out the candles on this on your birthday.
10. Bright lights launched in the sky at night.
11. Day of love. (2 words)
13. Hindu Festival of Lights.
14. A large, celebratory meal.

DOWN
  1. Fall feast of appreciation.
  3. A procession of people with a marching band and floats.
  4. Celebration of the birth of baby Jesus.
  5. Spooky autumn holiday with costumes.
  7. Holiday celebrating the workforce. (2 words)
  8. A traditional fruity dessert, often made with apples.
12. Hang these decorative paper strips to celebrate.

HOLIDAYS

A crossword puzzle with the following answers filled in:

- HANUKKAH
- THANKSGIVING
- PARADE
- CHRISTMAS
- HALLOWEEN
- BIRTHDAY
- LABORDAY
- PICNIC
- CAKE
- FIREWORKS
- VALENTINESDAY
- STREAMERS
- DIWALI
- FEAST

STATE CAPITALS

DOWN
1. Washington
2. New York
3. Alaska
4. California
6. Idaho
8. Texas
9. Ohio
10. North Carolina
12. Massachusetts

ACROSS
4. New Mexico (2 words)
5. Georgia
7. Kansas
10. Virginia
11. Colorado
13. Hawaii

STATE CAPITALS

INSECTS

ACROSS

4. Use bug spray to protect from this insect's bite.
6. Winged insect that comes from a chrysalis.
8. This turns into a butterfly.
11. Itsy bitsy insect that spins a web.
12. Insects use these to fly.
13. This green insect is said to look like it's praying.
14. House pest with six legs.

DOWN

1. This flying insect pollinates flowers.
2. In the same family as butterfly, this insect is usually less colorful.
3. Red insect with black spots.
5. Don't let these bugs show up to your picnic.
7. Find this flying insect buzzing around food.
9. These insects eat wood and can damage houses.
10. Some insects have two of these sticking out of their head.

INSECTS

BACK TO SCHOOL

ACROSS
1. Erasable writing utensil.
4. Season students typically aren't in school.
8. Assignment completed outside of school.
9. Fruit you give a teacher.
10. Leader of the classroom.
13. Rubber object that gets rid of pencil marks.
14. Exam.

DOWN
2. A spiral-bound collection of lined paper.
3. A mini test.
5. Letter you earn on a paper, such as A+ or C.
6. Writing utensil that uses ink.
7. Person in charge of the whole school.
9. Class with paint and crayons.
11. Where a student sits.
12. Time students spend on the playground.

BACK TO SCHOOL

Across:
- 1. PENCIL
- 4. SUMMER
- 8. HOMEWORK
- 9. APPLE
- 10. TEACHER
- 13. ERASER
- 14. TEST

Down:
- 2. NOTEBOOK
- 3. QUIZ
- 5. GRADE
- 6. PEN
- 7. PRINCIPAL
- 11. DESK
- 12. RECESS

Grid answers:
- PENCIL
- NOTEBOOK
- QUIZ
- SUMMER
- GRADE
- PEN
- PRINCIPAL
- HOMEWORK
- APPLE
- TEACHER
- ART
- DESK
- RECESS
- ERASER
- TEST

ANIMAL SOUNDS

ACROSS
  3. Tweet tweet.
  4. Meow.
  6. Honk.
  8. Ooh ooh ah ah.
  10. Baa.
  12. Squeak squeak.
  13. Woof woof.

DOWN
  1. Hissss.
  2. Ribbet.
  3. Buzz buzz.
  5. Neigh.
  7. Cock-a-doodle-doo.
  9. 'Rawr!' says the King of the Jungle.
  11. Oink.
  13. Quack quack.

ANIMAL SOUNDS

SWEET TREATS

ACROSS

1. Dessert flavor made from cacao.
3. Orange vegetable sometimes used in a spiced cake.
5. Popular pudding flavor, often with cookies and whipped cream.
6. Hard candy on a stick.
7. Varieties of this dessert include carrot, red velvet, and German chocolate.
9. Make a house out of this during the holidays.
10. Dairy ingredient often used in baking.
11. Ice cream with whipped cream, nuts, and a cherry.
12. Apple, pumpkin, or pecan.
13. Varieties of these desserts include chocolate chip and sugar.

DOWN

2. Fluffy dessert on a stick served at a fair. (2 words)
3. Sweet treat including chocolates, gummies, and sours.
4. Sweet breakfast pastry with a hole in the middle.
5. A dense, chocolate baked good often cut into squares.
8. Cake made with cream cheese, often with strawberries.

SWEET TREATS

VALENTINE'S DAY

ACROSS
3. What cupid carries along with his bow.
5. Cards exchanged on this holiday.
7. You might gift a box of these sweet treats.
10. A place you might take a date.
12. Someone might gift a dozen of these.
13. Valentine's Day color.

DOWN
1. Emotion of Valentine's Day.
2. A present.
3. Yearly celebration of a couple.
4. Fill this with helium.
6. These make up a bouquet.
7. Flying baby who shoots arrows.
8. Valentine's shape.
9. When a couple goes out for a nice evening.
11. This bird symbolizes love or peace.

VALENTINE'S DAY

1 down: LOVE
2 down: GIFT
3 across: ARROW
3 down: ANNIVERSARY
4 down: BALLOON
5 across: VALENTINES
6 down: FLOWER
7 across: CHOCOLATES
7 down: CUPID
8 down: HEART
9 down: DATE
10 across: RESTAURANT
11 down: DOVE
12 across: ROSES
13 across: RED

BIRDS

ACROSS
3. Flightless aquatic bird.
6. National bird of the United States. (2 words)
9. Bird's mouth.
10. Bird builds this to lay eggs.
12. How a penguin walks.
13. What a baby chick says.
14. This bird can't fly but it can grow to 9 feet tall.

DOWN
1. What a bird lays.
2. Bird found at the beach.
4. What a bird says. (2 words)
5. Pink bird that might stand on one leg.
7. Bird that might repeat human words.
8. A large bird whose males have colorful tail feathers.
11. Where a bird builds a nest.
14. This nocturnal bird says 'Hoo! Hoo!'.

BIRDS

BODIES OF WATER

ACROSS
  2. A smaller, shallower lake.
  7. Ocean furthest south on the globe.
  9. Natural flowing course of water leading to an ocean, sea, or lake.
  10. Number of lakes making up the Great Lakes.
  11. Ocean bordering the United States' east coast.
  12. An area filled with water surrounded by land.

DOWN
  1. A frozen pond where you can ice skate.
  2. Famous canal in South America. (2 words)
  3. Ocean furthest north on the globe.
  4. The five of them make up most of the world's water.
  5. Largest mammal found in the ocean.
  6. Largest and deepest ocean in the world.
  8. River in Africa spanning 11 countries including Egypt and Ethiopia.
  11. Longest river in the world.

BODIES OF WATER

VEGETABLES

ACROSS
1. This vegetable grows as a cob.
3. Broth cooked with onions, carrots, and other vegetables.
6. Dish consisting of lettuce, chopped veggies, and dressing.
8. Orange gourd that appears during the fall.
11. Diet consisting of no meat.
12. This made Popeye strong.
14. Can be served baked, mashed, or as french fries.

DOWN
2. Vegetable sometimes cut into rings, breaded, and fried.
4. These little veggies come in a pod.
5. This vegetable is used to make pickles.
7. Vegetable that forms the base of a salad.
9. Red fruit often confused for a vegetable.
10. Spicy pepper.
13. Orange vegetable used for a snowman's nose.

VEGETABLES

A crossword puzzle with the following answers:

- CORN
- ONION
- SOUP
- PEAS
- SALAD
- CUCUMBER
- PUMPKIN
- LETTUCE
- TOMATO
- VEGETARIAN
- JALAPENO
- SPINACH
- CARROT
- POTATO

MY HOUSE

ACROSS
3. A room to keep clothes.
4. Narrow area that connects rooms.
8. Small table next to the bed that might hold a lamp.
10. Appliance that heats food up quickly.
11. Where someone sleeps in the house.
14. Where you keep a car.

DOWN
1. Room right below the roof, often used for storage.
2. A house might have one for swimming.
3. Storage for plates and cups in the kitchen.
5. Room that might have a TV and couch. (2 words)
6. This fabric item is spread on the floor under the furniture.
7. Room with a sink and toilet.
9. Room for cooking.
12. Furniture meant for work or studying.
13. Area behind or in front of a house.

MY HOUSE

Across:
- 1. ATTIC
- 3. CLOSET
- 4. HALLWAY
- 8. NIGHTSTAND
- 10. MICROWAVE
- 11. BEDROOM
- 14. GARAGE

Down:
- 1. ATTIC
- 2. POOL
- 3. CABINET
- 5. LIVINGROOM
- 6. RUG
- 7. BATHROOM
- 9. KITCHEN
- 12. DESK
- 13. YARD

DOCTOR'S VISIT

DOWN

1. When your temperature is too high.
2. You might see a doctor and this professional at your visit.
3. Tool used to take temperature.
5. This common ailment might be met with a cough and sneezing.
7. Put this over a small cut or scrape to protect the wound.
8. Yearly doctor appointment.
9. What a patient might get when they break an arm or leg.
10. Seasonal ailment in response to pollen.
11. Virus that produces itchy red spots. (2 words)

ACROSS

4. Pain in the forehead area.
6. Doctors wear this around their neck to hear a heartbeat.
12. Prescription to make you feel better.
13. Schedule this with the doctor's office.
14. Large building providing medical care.
15. Eyesight.

DOCTOR'S VISIT

1 FEVER
2 NURSE
3 THERMOMETER
4 HEADACHE
5 COLD
6 STETHOSCOPE
7 BANDAID
8 CHECKUP
9 CAST
10 ALLERGIE
11 CHICKENPOX
12 MEDICINE
13 APPOINTMENT
14 HOSPITAL
15 VISION

WORDS THAT START WITH "S"

ACROSS
2. Take a small drink.
3. Slow-moving animal that lives upside down in trees.
4. Trip or fall.
5. Activity on a snowy hill.
6. Carbonated beverage.
7. Varieties of this food include peanut butter and grilled cheese.
8. Shoes worn to the beach.
11. Dinner.

DOWN
1. Icy rain.
2. Rock.
4. Amphibian that looks like a lizard.
6. Boat.
8. Cinderella lost hers.
9. July is in this season.
10. Opposite of 'start'.

WORDS THAT START WITH "S"

JOBS

ACROSS

3. Helps sick people get better.
4. Designs buildings.
5. Keeps people's teeth clean and healthy.
7. Painter or sculptor.
9. Makes sure swimmers are safe.
11. _____ workers help build things like roads and buildings.
12. Argues in court for their clients.
13. Trained for the space program.
14. Transports people from one place to another. (2 words)
15. Delivers mail and packages.

DOWN

1. Writer for a newspaper.
2. Makes pastries, cakes, and breads.
6. Works with doctors to help sick patients.
8. Instructs kids in the classroom.
10. Helps keep a building clean and running.

JOBS

IN THE KITCHEN

ACROSS

3. _____ and pans.
5. Where you heat your saucepans and frying pans.
7. This appliance mixes and chops food at a fast speed.
9. Drink made from beans and hot water.
11. The main purpose of a kitchen.
13. Keeps your groceries cool.
14. Wash your dishes in this basin with a spout.
15. Set this before dinner by placing plates and silverware.

DOWN

1. Last course of the meal.
2. Where you can bake a pie or roast a chicken.
4. Forks, knives, and spoons.
6. Meal typically eaten at noon.
8. Last meal of the day.
10. Crisp your bread in this appliance.
12. First meal of the day.

IN THE KITCHEN

WORDS THAT START WITH "B"

ACROSS
2. Ride this to school or work.
5. Flying animal that builds a nest.
6. Sport with 3 bases and home plate.
8. It rings to signal people.
9. Keeps you warm at night.
10. Important component of a sandwich.
11. Spread this dairy product on toast.

DOWN
1. Large animal that hibernates in the winter.
2. A place where breads, cakes, and pies are made.
3. Shy.
4. These tart fruits can be used in pies or jams.
5. Capital of Massachusetts.
6. Kind of dog with wrinkles and a flat snout.
7. Color of a clear sky.
11. Infant.

WORDS THAT START WITH "B"

ACROSS
1. What one wears at night.
5. Wear these on your feet when it's drizzling. (2 words)
6. A person's entire collection of clothes.
7. Skirt for a ballerina.
10. Hang a jacket or hat on this at a home's entrance. (2 words)
13. These keep one's ears warm.
15. Wooden chest with drawers that holds clothes.

DOWN
2. Wear this to the pool or beach.
3. They go over your socks.
4. Jacket worn when it's very windy.
8. Article that goes on the head.
9. In the morning you get _____ by putting on clothes.
11. They keep your hands warm.
12. Room that holds clothes.
14. Wear this to protect clothes when cooking.

CLOTHING

WORDS THAT START WITH "L"

ACROSS
2. Spotted cat that lives in jungles, rainforests, and deserts.
3. A key fits into this.
4. Dog that retrieves.
6. Rail vehicle that pulls trains.
7. Hard candy on a stick.
8. Opposite of smooth.
9. Gecko or chameleon.

DOWN
1. Layered Italian dish.
2. Where you can check out books.
3. What you climb to reach high places.
4. Screw this into a lamp to illuminate it. (2 words)
5. Tart citrus fruit.
6. Having good fortune.
7. Take this camping to see in the dark.
8. A pile of these may be used for firewood.

WORDS THAT START WITH "L"

SCHOOL SUBJECTS

ACROSS
1. Class where you might paint and draw.
3. Class that might include singing and learning an instrument.
5. You study battles, presidents, and government in this class.
6. Class that focuses on books.
9. Gym class. (2 words)
11. Class involving numbers and equations.
12. A movement class set to music.
14. Class that includes reading and writing.

DOWN
2. Part of the day where kids play outside.
4. Class focusing on the yearbook or newspaper.
7. Class that might study biology, molecules, and matter.
8. The study of land locations and physical features of the earth.
10. Period for doing homework or studying. (2 words)
13. Mid-day meal.

SCHOOL SUBJECTS

SEE A MOVIE

ACROSS

4. Trailers before the movie.
6. Where you go to see a movie.
7. What an attendant might shine in a dark theater.
8. They roll at the end of the movie listing actors and crew.
10. Grab a bucket of this salty movie snack.
14. Genre of movie that has a lot of jokes.
15. Genre that may have car crashes and fight scenes.

DOWN

1. People who star in movies.
2. This gets you into the theater.
3. Machine that puts the movie on the screen.
5. Wear special versions of these when watching a 3D movie.
9. Genre of film where two characters fall in love.
11. Something sweet to go with your popcorn.
12. Chips with melted cheese.
13. Carbonated drink from a fountain.

SEE A MOVIE

ON A SAFARI

ACROSS
3. Large reptile with a long tail and sharp teeth.
6. Large ape.
8. This spotted animal has a long neck to reach the tops of trees.
9. The largest land mammal.
11. Reptile with no legs.
12. Fast spotted cat.
14. Black and white striped animal similar to a horse.
15. This spotted animal sounds like it's laughing.

DOWN
1. Large mammal known for its horn.
2. This giant mammal lives in both the water and on land.
4. This person leads a safari.
5. Fast antelope that is prey to many animals.
7. These animals live in a pride.
10. You might pitch one to sleep in on a safari.
13. Continent where the Sahara Desert is located.

ON A SAFARI

THANKSGIVING

ACROSS
4. Popular Thanksgiving dessert.
6. Feeling when you are giving thanks.
7. Where you sit to eat your meal.
8. Sport that people watch on Thanksgiving.
10. Green veggies often used in a casserole. (2 words)
11. Orange gourd that may decorate your table.
13. Side dish that might be found inside the turkey.
14. Sauce to accompany turkey.

DOWN
1. Fruit that goes in a traditional pie.
2. Grain very similar to corn.
3. Fall.
4. Can be eaten mashed, twice baked, or loaded.
5. Tart fruits that make a Thanksgiving sauce.
9. People you may spend Thanksgiving with.
12. Main dish during Thanksgiving.

THANKSGIVING

Across
6. GRATEFUL
7. TABLE
8. FOOTBALL
10. GREENBEANS
11. PUMPKIN
13. STUFFING
14. GRAVY

Down
1. MAIZE
2. APPLE
3. AUTUMN
4. PIE
5. CRANBERRIES
9. FAMILY
12. TURKEY

TRAVEL

ACROSS
4. Where people go for air travel.
6. Where you might stay when traveling.
8. Opposite direction of West.
10. North, South, East, and West.
11. Paper tool depicting geography and directions.
13. Document that allows you to enter another country.
14. Where you board a train.

DOWN
1. Opposite direction of North.
2. Travel by water in this.
3. Sedan or SUV.
5. A vacation taken in the car. (2 words)
7. What you travel in while in the sky.
9. Tool used to tell directions.
12. Travel in this on a railroad.
15. What you present to board a plane or train.

TRAVEL

THE COLOR RED

ACROSS
- 3. Rudolph has a red one.
- 6. Food that is the basis of marinara sauce.
- 8. Red berry often made into jam.
- 11. Truck that firefighters drive. (2 words)
- 13. Red bird.
- 14. Condiment eaten with french fries.

DOWN
- 1. Romantic flower.
- 2. Organ in the human body that pumps blood.
- 4. Jelly.
- 5. Red road sign. (2 words)
- 7. Fruit often eaten with shortcake.
- 9. _____ of my eye.
- 10. Makeup worn on a mouth.
- 12. Crustacean that pinches.

THE COLOR RED

LET'S HAVE BREAKFAST

ACROSS
3. Pork strip.
6. Pour this in your cereal.
7. What kids watch while they eat breakfast.
9. Hot morning beverage.
10. These often come frozen to be cooked in the toaster.
11. Food with a hole in the middle, sometimes with sprinkles.
13. Sweet, circular food often eaten with maple syrup.

DOWN
1. Often toasted and topped with cream cheese.
2. Fruity breakfast drink. (2 words)
4. Crunchy breakfast food eaten with milk.
5. Room where breakfast is cooked.
6. Types of this include blueberry, bran, or chocolate chip.
8. Gelatinous fruit spread.
12. You might put butter and jelly on this.
14. You can eat them scrambled or hard boiled.

LET'S HAVE BREAKFAST

1. BAGEL
3. BACON
7. CARTOONS
10. WAFFLES
11. DOUGHNUT
13. PANCAKE
6. MILK
9. COFFEE
2. ORANGE
4. CEREAL
5. KITCHEN
6. MUFFIN
8. JELLY
12. TOAST
14. EGGS

BIRTHDAY PARTY

ACROSS

2. Make this when you blow out the candles.
3. 365 days.
5. A floating decoration.
6. He might pull a rabbit out of a hat.
9. Cold dessert served with cake. (2 words)
10. He makes balloon animals and has a painted face.
11. Slice this up after singing 'Happy Birthday to You.'
12. The top of a cupcake.
14. Gift.

DOWN

1. Hit this with a stick and candy will fall out.
4. What you send asking people to attend a party.
7. What people do before you blow out candles.
8. A fruity drink that is served in a bowl.
10. Light these on top of the cake.
13. Pin the tail on the _____.

BIRTHDAY PARTY

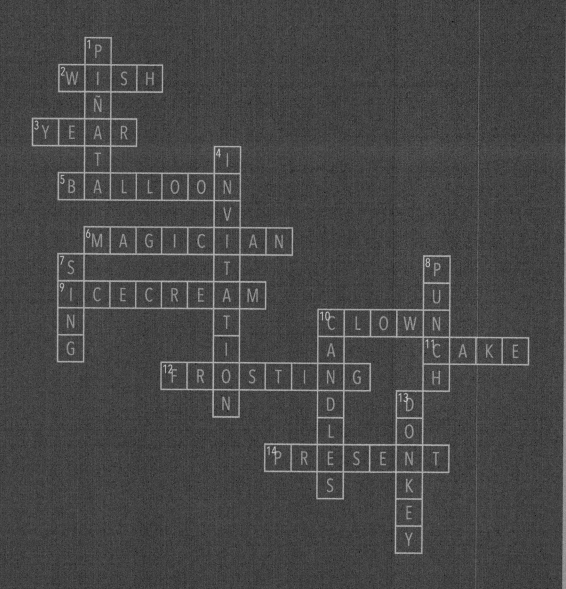

WORDS THAT BEGIN WITH "P"

ACROSS
  3. Wooden writing utensil.
  4. Baby dog.
  7. A twisted, salty snack.
  8. You need this to go skydiving.
  9. Where you store coins. (2 words)
  10. Flavor of a candy cane.
  12. A small horse.
  13. Jigsaw.

DOWN
  1. Form of medicine.
  2. A shelled nut.
  5. Large rodent with spiky quills.
  6. Flying dinosaur.
  8. Bread with sauce and cheese.
  11. Black and white waddling bird.
  13. Least valuable coin.

WORDS THAT BEGIN WITH "P"

LET'S GO CAMPING

ACROSS

1. Lock up your food so this grizzly animal doesn't steal it.
4. Pitch this for sleeping.
5. Boat with oars.
6. Pack this to locate north, south, east, and west.
10. Gooey ingredient in a s'more.
13. Shine this to see in the dark.
14. You need this to start a campfire.

DOWN

1. Tool that helps you see long distances.
2. These twinkle in the sky at night.
3. Small pests that might invade your picnic.
7. Trying to catch dinner from a stream or lake.
8. A spooky tale told around a fire. (2 words)
9. Roast a marshmallow over this.
11. A strenuous walk.
12. Wear these on your feet when hiking.

LET'S GO CAMPING

Across / Down answers:

- 1. BEAR
- 2. STARS
- 3. ANTS
- 4. TENT
- 5. CANOE
- 6. COMPASS
- 7. FISHIN
- 8. GHOST STORY
- 9. CAMPFIRE
- 10. MARSH
- 11. HIKE
- 1. BINOCULARS
- 13. FLASHLIGHT
- 12. BOOTS
- 14. FIREWOOD

Grid letters:

```
B E A R        S   A
I              T E N T
C A N O E      A   T
O              R   S
C O M P A S S  S
U                        F
L                G       I
A              C H       S
M A R S H M A L L O W    H      B
S      I   M   L O       I      O
       K   P   S T       N      O
       E   F L A S H L I G H T  T
           I   T                S
       F I R E W O O D
           E   R
               Y
```

Made in the USA
Monee, IL
02 October 2022

15063880R00057